said the

paper

to the

pen

poems by Mr. B

Mike Bertram

B-Hive Publishing

First paperback edition March 2019

Illustration copyright © 2019 by Melanie Glowacki
Illustration copyright © 2019 by Jamie Bertram
Book design and layout by Studio Creative Group

ISBN: 978-1-947312-06-7 (Paperback)
LCCN: 2019903551

Published by B-Hive Publishing
Also by Penmanship Books

We all had that ONE teacher.
I had two.
Mr. Chef-chick and Mrs. Martko
There's no Mr. B
without you.

This is dedicated to you.

What former students say about Mr. B

"Mr. B's classroom was a safe space before we even knew that we needed a safe space. In his classroom, you believed in yourself and believed in your dreams because Mr. B taught you how. I entered Mike Bertram's classroom for the very last time in 2003. Fifteen years later, I still use his guidance and support to help navigate my life...and I will take that gift with me forever. I truly hope that every young person finds their "Mr. B". He is everything you didn't know you needed."

~Anthony Alexander 2001-2003

"When I think of him, the impact that he has had on my life, I know that his presence has been monumental because I'm not just grateful to have been taught by him on my best days, but on my worst too. I am forever indebted to the man who not only helped me with words but told me I had something to say when the rest of the world was silencing me."

~Crystal Myles 2003-2004

"Mr. B's 3rd grade class is still my favorite! He made learning fun. Mr. B would take the poems we wrote and make us poetry books because he wanted us to appreciate everyone's writing. He also helped me win the Junior Journalist Contest in second grade and nicknamed me 'Gobbles' because my poem was about a turkey. I will always remember him stealing my snack or as he would say, *"permanently borrowing it"* with his stomach."

~Nicole Pignataro 2014-2015

On Poetry and the Classroom...

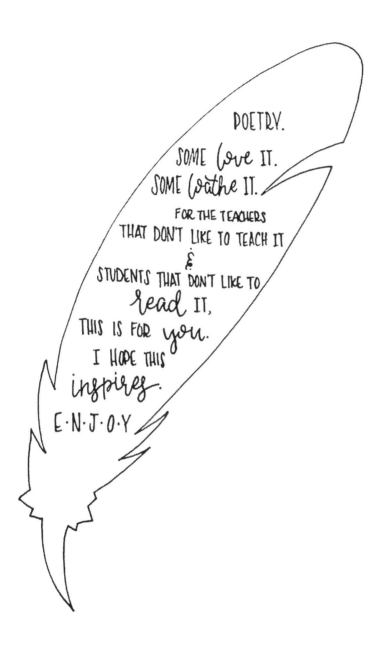

POETRY.

SOME love IT.

SOME loathe IT.

FOR THE TEACHERS
THAT DON'T LIKE TO TEACH IT
&
STUDENTS THAT DON'T LIKE TO
read IT,

THIS IS FOR you.

I HOPE THIS
inspires.

E·N·J·O·Y

From Teacher to Teacher

"You don't pick the grade you teach... the grade picks you"- Chris Ryan

I am way too big to teach Kindergarten. If I fall, it would be like a redwood tree crushing a village of Smurfs. And when it comes to teenagers, my patience is similar to a McDonald's McRib sandwich because I can deal with them for a limited time only. But third grade? I love teaching third grade! I love the I-can-do-it-myself-but-can-you-help-me attitude that eight-year-olds possess. I love the wide-eyed curiosity and the you-asked-for-it honesty. I love that third graders still pick their noses and laugh when I spell words aloud containing the letters "pp". I love when they argue that unicorns are real and should be added to the animal research project list. Third graders make me belly laugh day-to-day. They inspire and motivate me to be the best teacher possible. They give me hope and keep me going. They are poetry.

As teachers, we strive to be the spark that ignites dreams. It's generally understood that we are not in this teaching thing for the money or to see how many "World's Greatest Teacher" mugs we can collect. I've yet to meet a teacher who pumps their fist and says, "Oh! I can't wait until testing season begins!" No, we want to inspire. We want to kickstart the imaginations of the next generation of leaders, thinkers, scientists, writers and artists who will make the world a better place. We want to be that teacher our students remember forever.

Every year, a new swarm of bees arrive to conduct buzz-iness in my classroom, known as the B-Hive. (Get it? I'm Mr. B and Room 20 is the B-Hive.) I prepare my classroom to not only be a place for them to learn, but a safe space for all students to express themselves, mature, and have the freedom to blossom into the unique individuals they truly are. Here, we use the power of poetry to learn from each other, embrace our differences, build self-esteem, create connections, and to find that special voice hidden inside of us all. Not only does poetry allow students to explore how they feel, but it gives me the opportunity to see the world through their eyes. Poetry allows them to experiment with the unending possibility of language. These young minds are full of energy and curiosity, ready to pollinate the seeds of learning and take on adventures adults could never dream of. They see life in a way we have forgotten.

My favorite moments in class are when we rewrite the works of, as the kids say, "...really old dead people that wrote confusing poems." We can take an apology poem like, "This is Just to Say" (aka The Plum Poem) by William Carlos Williams and remix it to create a connection that relates to them. Now, instead of plums, we have Trinity writing about eating all the wings at Pizza Hut when her bestie is talking, and Ryan apologizing to his boxing gloves, as he says, "FORGIVE ME for punching the gym wall. It hurts you way more than it hurt me. If you had teeth, they would be gone." Poetry gives my students the freedom of creativity while allowing them to say, "Hey, that old poem wasn't so bad." It allows them to appreciate language instead of being intimidated by it and allows me to fall in love with new poems each year.

Publishing classroom books, performing for other classes, creating virtual poetry museums, making videos, and sharing in the excitement of young authors who win writing contests are magical school moments that remind me how fortunate I am to be a teacher. Watching my students learn about each other through their writing not only helps them academically, but creates that family environment that every classroom needs to be successful.

The demands of teaching, especially in today's are-you-ready-for-another-standardized-test climate, have made this career more challenging and stressful. High expectations are placed on teachers and students without the resources or support needed to succeed. It is easy to lose focus on why we chose, or shall I say, why we were chosen to teach. Sometimes we need our students to remind us that what we do is important and worthwhile. It took my super smart, sweet student, Tanvi, to remind me. We were putting together a collection of poems she wrote throughout the year, when she looked at me and said, "Mr. B, you are always taking our poems and making them into books for us. You have a lot of poems, too. Why don't you make a book? You always tell us words in books last forever. Don't you want your words to last forever?"

"Don't be afraid."

"Take chances."

"Try new things."

"Follow your dreams."

These phrases are often echoed throughout classrooms by teachers year after year. But how many of us live the words we preach to our students? How are they going to take chances, if we don't? Tanvi's words motivated me. If I want to ignite change, then I better put the doubt down, grab that dream I let collect dust in the corner, Times New Roman it up real nice, and show the world that my words can move mountains.

That being said, after twenty-plus years of writing with students in the B-Hive and the wisdom of an adorable eight-year-old, it is time to make my words last forever. I don't fancy myself this great writer, superior educator or amazing poet. I'm just a chubby, bald, snack stealing teacher who loves school, is devoted to my students, dedicated to the art of teaching, and really enjoys reading poetry written by young people who still think the floor is lava and any amount of homework I give them is way too much. *Said the Paper to the Pen* is a collection of poems for students, teachers or anyone who would like to peek inside my favorite place in the world, my classroom. If anything, I hope this inspires someone, anyone, and everyone to "**GET WITH THE BUZZ and RELEASE YOUR POETRY!**"

This is the beginning of a journey that I hope we will remember forever.

With all the words in my heart,
Mr. B

"I've learned that people will **FORGET** what you **SAID,**

people will **FORGET** what you **DID,**

but people will **NEVER FORGET**

how you made them **FEEL.**"

- Maya Angelou

Contents

I Teach…

If you asked me 25 years ago why I became a teacher,
I'd give the standard student-teacher, fresh out of college,
I-love-kids. Can-I-please-have-this-job?
Answer.

But, two districts, seventy-five observations,
and six-hundred, sixty-three students later…

I know the answer to the question,

Why do I teach?

I teach because the future comedians
need an audience and drama queens need a stage.

I teach because I LOVE snack and recess
and I'm fighting to bring back nap time!

I teach because, in the eyes of my students,
War is just a card game,
 and the WORST thing to be is… IT!

I teach because it is way cooler to talk about SpongeBob
SquarePants than the latest presidential tweet.

I teach because I like to answer questions:

"Mr.B why do you wear that same shirt all the time?"
"I only have 4 shirts."
"Why do you only have four shirts?"
"I have 6 kids."
"Why do you have 6 kids?"
"Take your Math book out!"

I teach because homemade cupcakes are heaven,
and birthday smiles are priceless.

I teach because every child is special
and labels belong on clearance racks.

I teach because watching a student handle their pencil like a
wand transforming their print into cursive is magical.

I teach because the corporate world is phony,
And kids are honest… too honest,

but they LOVE unconditionally.

Where else can you have a bad day and still get a hug?
Where else can you make up answers
to questions you don't really know the answers to?

And here,
I have no choice but to smile.

I wear a student-made necklace like a badge of honor
and tape Crayola scented pictures to my desk
like they were paintings by Van Gogh.

I teach because 8-year-olds have clay minds,
and I can shape them,

shape them to believe that LOVE
is as simple as sharing your colored pencils
AND rainbow goldfish.

I teach because
Green Eggs and Ham are delicious
and the web that Charlotte wove
is way more significant to American society
than how many different shades of grey there are.

You figure that out!
I'll teach the importance of friendship.

I hate lessons plans, but love planning lessons.
I've acquired a taste for school lunches,
and look out my window
praying for snow days.

I teach because of Sophia.
Every day she hugged me,
told me she loved me
and said,

"Mr. B, I never want to leave third grade."

This is the age of budget cuts, overcrowding,
lost innocence and dense ears

but from 8:30 to 2:55 … I teach

to leave a mark,
have my students cement it in their hearts,

and remember me forever.

Said the Paper to the Pen...

"My life is in your hands,
Paint my future with each curve,
Fill me with thoughts,
Mark me with memories,

TRUST ME.

Let me feel...
Your joy, your pain,
Your love, your rage.
Let me hold your dreams.

Give voice to the voiceless,
Write the world's wrongs,
Let your ink remain forever,
***TOGETHER** we can change the world.*

I am your canvas.
Without you, I am nothing.
Without me, where will you go?"

Said the paper to the pen,

"My life is in your hands.
Don't waste me.
Please, don't waste me."

My Favorite Teacher

i remember my first teacher
never rewarded me with
stickers and 100s

BUT

kisses and hugs
that felt better, lasted longer,

more than school work, she taught me to be
honest and polite,
and to get love, you must give love.

year after year,
i smile thinking of
my favorite teacher,

my first teacher,

the center of my universe,
my mother.

Welcome to Room 20

Welcome to Room 20

Where everyone dances
to the beat of their own Fortnite
character BUT sings the same song.

This is Family.

A family that plays together,
works together, *annnd* thanks to Siana-Lee...

a family that draws faces on their index fingers
and waves together.

We *"Cha-Cha-Cha"* on birthdays
and *"OOOOOOOOO"* at the first sign of trouble.

This is Room 20.

Where paper clips are straightened,
twisted, bent, and used for everything...
EXCEPT clipping papers.

This is Room 20.

Where the kids put the key in the ignition and drive you...
straight to the Teachers' Room
in search of *C H O C O L A T E.*

When the kids in Room 20 are supposed to be writing,
they draw.

When the kids in Room 20 are supposed to be drawing,
they color.

When the kids in Room 20 need to color,
one of them raises their hand and cries out,

"I don't know what to do!"

And it's okay,
because this is Room 20.

Rule #1 is: **Remember, you are Loved.**

And they do.
And they smile.
And they laugh.

And they share snacks, with **EVERYONE**…
Except Mr.B, because
*"He's **soooo** greedy."*

And it's true. I love snacks.

Just like I love when Arielle asks,
"Can someone read with me?" and without hesitation,
16 third graders all raise their hand to volunteer.

This is Room 20.

Our line is **NEVER** STRAIGHT
But tell me,

what road in life's journey is?

So, welcome!
Welcome to Room 20.

Be different.
Be unique.

Just make sure you answer **ALL** the questions
on your Standardized State Test.

Teacher, Teacher

(Mr.B's version of The Tyger by William Blake)

Teacher Teacher, Mr. B!
    Always writing poetry.

Bald and chubby,
    creeps at night,

devouring every
    donut in sight.

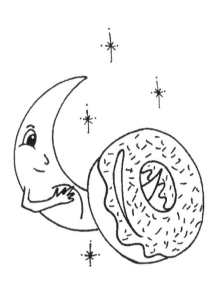

He'll steal your snack
    right off your desk.

EAT IT!
    Now, there's nothing left.

Teacher Teacher, Mr. B!
    That snack stealing, bald guy, writing poetry!

Get with the Buzz

Poems BEE buzzing
in the hive full of bees,
scratching down words
like a puppy full of fleas.

Notebooks, sidewalks,
sometimes I like to type,
poems spilling out
every morning, noon, and night.

They're sweeter than nectar,
stinging like a honey bee,
so get with the buzz...

Release your POETRY!

Monsters in My Classroom

EVERY. DAY.

THEY STARE.

38 eyes…watching,
waiting,
studying,
my EVERY MOVE.

They notice the shirt I wore three days ago.

"MR. B! YOU HAVE A STAIN!"

They never forget
snack time, recess, or gym class,
but ALWAYS forget
homework, pencils and lunch money.

If ever a word is misspelled or
punctuation mark forgotten,

with more precision than a pack of ruthless red pens,
THEY ATTACK!

When the classroom reaches a **CATEGORY 5** noise level
I often wonder why I didn't take my mother's advice
and become a doctor.

Then, I remember...

Doctors don't get greeted with high 5s and hallway laughter.
Doctors don't get bear hugs on Fridays as they leave work.
Doctors don't get drawings taped to their desk daily.

TEACHERS DO!

And without a class of loving, little monsters
School would be **TOTALLY LAME!**

what is a Life-ku?

A 'Life-Ku' is very necessary life advice from Mr. B
to his third grade students in 5-7-5 Haiku form. This advice
often includes references to food and confuses them
immensely.

Life-ku #1

Student: "Mr. B, he's being weird!"

Mr. B: "LIFE is a box of

Cheez-it crackers... full of SQUARES

and BURSTS of FLAVOR."

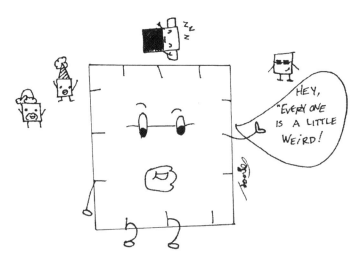

This is Just to Say

(Mr. B's version after William Carlos Williams)

For Nicole (the girl I steal snacks from),

This is Just to Say
I have eaten
the Little Bites Mini Crumb Cakes
that were sitting on your desk

which, indeed,
you were saving
for snack time.

FORGIVE ME!

The cinnamon
scent swept slowly
across the room,
pulling my belly

closer… closer… C L O S E R

until
they LEAPED

out of the bag
and into my mouth.

Love,
Your greedy 3ʳᵈ grade teacher

WORDS

NOTHING - is just - a WORD.

You might think of them
as scrambled letters.

You might sound out their syllables,
but they are so much more.

WORDS.

Glide d
              o
                 w
                   n
                         like confetti,
when the time is just right.

      Use them.
You will NEVER be invisible.

WORDS.

Comforting like Grandma's kisses,
          or earth-shattering like
                    THUNDERBOLTS
      delivered from the tongue.

Be prepared.

Someone WILL say,
        "*Hush now.*"

THEN...
Let them spill out
like crashing waves.

woRds.

Hurt and Heal,
        Love and Hate,
Unite and Divide,

Use them wisely.
Etch them into eternity.

EaCH oNE.

Speaking,
        Writing,
Speaking,
        Writing

Once said they will NEvER be forgotten, because

NotHiNG –
        is just –
                a woRd.

What a Good Friend Makes

A good friend makes you laugh
when your smile is upside down.
A good friend doesn't judge
when you're acting like a clown.

A good friend shares their snack with you
even when you give them nothing back.
A good friend helps defend you
from hurtful, word attacks.

Just like treasures hidden deep,
good friends are hard to find.
I'm glad to have a friend like you
always by my side.

So be good, my good friend,
even though we have to part,

Our friendship will remain
locked, deep down, forever
in my heart.

DREAMS

Life starts with a dream
      tattooed to your heart

so hold fast,
      hold long,
            stay strong

  let the dream keeper

capture
  your heart melodies
          so they can
sing
    forever…

If Only

If only
I said, "Hello"
instead of walking on by.

If only
I spoke up
instead of acting so shy.

If only
I yelled, "Stop!"
instead of freezing with a stare.

If only
I stopped for a moment
and showed you someone cared.

I could have
made a difference,
breathed life back in your day.

If only,
I tried to help
take your pain away.

All I Teach...

THEY say all I teach is poetry.
They're right!

But what **THEY** call a poem,
I call life.

From my son's first step
to my grandma's last breath,

the ink in my pen
stays in tune with the beat of my chest.

A place where words flow like a fountain,
so come take a drink.

BUT, you better be careful,
one sip makes you think,

about your life and my life
and how are you going to change it?

Do you run from the world
OR stand up and face it?

Life ain't no crystal stair.
Look at little Mattie*.

He faced death every day
BUT, still went through it happy.

Compared to that, my job is easy you see.
I wake up every day and say…

> *"This looks like a job for B…*
> *to teach everybody Poetry,*
> *so grab your number 2 and follow me...*
> *because Poetry is all I see…"*

What would you do if I told you
with a pen and a paper

you could leave a mark on this world
that will be here one hundred years later?

Would you sit at home watching YouTube
Playing your Playstation from Sony?

OR

Would you pick up a pen and write a poem
that paints a picture so clear the whole world can see?

Don't sit inside that box
and dot your *i*'s and cross your *t*'s.
Take a step outside and use your creativity.

So when your parents don't listen
and your teacher is telling,

release that anger on paper,
let your pen do the yelling.

And don't sweat the small stuff,
it will tear you apart.

I'm not really worried about your grades,
I'm more concerned about what's in your heart.

This world doesn't need more A…B…Cs….and Ds;
what this world needs is more L - O - V – E!

So if **THEY say** all I teach is poetry,
I guess it's true.

But **THEY** don't understand
the poetry I teach…… **IS YOU.**

* Mattie Stepanek was an American award winning poet who published seven best-selling
books of poetry and peace essays before his death at age 13

VERBS TO LIVE BY

LIVE LEARN LAUGH LOVE

TALK WRITE ASK HUG

TRY WORK HELP CARE

SMILE THINK COMPLIMENT SHARE

LISTEN UNDERSTAND COMFORT CREATE

BEFRIEND ACCEPT INSPIRE

...bee GREAT.

Life-ku #2

Student :   "It's okay. I'll wait."

Mr. B:

"LIFE is like a bowl

of cereal... wait TOO LONG,

it gets all SOGGY."

The Curse

Jelly donuts with powder
jump start my morning
right before work.

First bite,
jelly **SQUIRRRTS** on my shirt.
I look down,

Smile at the stain
and say,

"I have inherited my mother's curse."

Beautiful Again

eight-year-olds are MAGICIANS

using a sleight of hand
they remind us what the world
is supposed to be

dancing and singing
        dancing and singing
skipping through life without a care

asking questions
        accepting differences
forgiving and forgetting

they are DREAMERS

filled with secret adventures
        racing with the wind

twirling through time
        erasing the past
writing the future

watch them

absorb their innocence
from seed to stem

and make this world beautiful
again

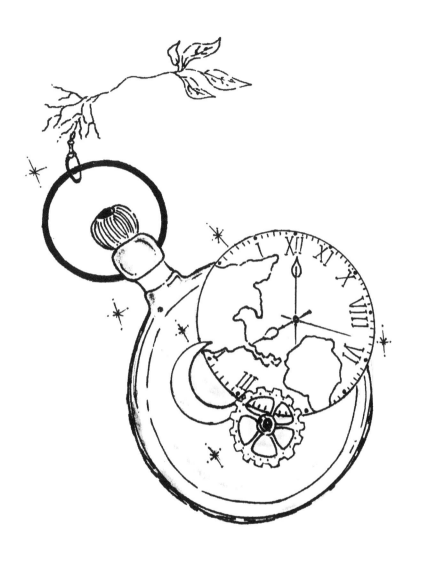

Don't Ask Me

Have a Holly Jolly Christmas
but
don't ask me to play Santa
just because
I'm built like a snowman.
I wish I could melt away pounds
like Frosty in spring,
but cookies sing songs to my belly,
and cocoa dances down my throat,
making this fat man…
Jolly!!

How to Eat a Poem

(Mr. B's version after Eve Merriam's Classic)

How do you eat a poem?
Let's hit the buffet.
It's time to eat a poem,
And we'll do it my way.

I flip it. I flap it.
Rip the wrapper
then I snack it.

Treat a poem like an egg
and crack, crack, crack it.

Chowing down words,
I Slurp. I Burp.
Blend it all together,
make it tasty like dessert.

No fork,
    No knife,
No need for a spoon.
Like pepper,
    I crush it,
Stirring up a tasty tune.

That's how you eat a poem.
That's how you eat a poem.
That's how …you eat …a poem.

What Teachers REALLY Do

Teachers are **AWESOME!**
Teachers are *COOOL*.

Teachers are lunchtime
CSI crime unit playground detectives
solving kickball cases,
gathering witnesses from the latest recess drama.

We analyze handwriting samples
looking for clues to find out…

"Whose paper is this?"
"Whose paper is this?"

Teachers have adhesives
to keep work hanging through the seasons,

- from Scotch tape to masking,
we keep it real sticky.

Teachers are **INNOVATIVE** and **THRIFTY**.

Pass me a paper clip.

I'll fix the zipper on your jacket,
poke holes in orange glue caps,
unjam the stapler, the pencil sharpener,
annnd tighten the screw in your desk...

Who needs a screwdriver?!
I have a pocket full of paper clips!

Teachers are born with gifts.

SUPER SPEED!
      SUPER STRENGTH!
            SUPER EVERYTHING!

We can quiet an entire cafeteria
simply by raising our hand.

We can straighten the most crooked line,
twist the too-tight top off your thermos,

and stop beastly behaviors with a stare so cold...
          IT WILL FREEZE YOUR SOUL!

Teachers are Superheroes that *SWOOP* in
and **SAVE THE DAY!**

Then RUIN IT with extra homework.

AND when students aren't around to see …

Teachers live like **ROYALTY!**

Chilling in our secret teachers' room lair.
We have manicure and pedicure stations
to attend to our tired hands and feet,

as we watch *"the news"*
on 65-inch ultra high-definition smart TVs,
eating gourmet lunches from our own personal chefs.

Man, I'll tell you this teacher life is the best.

Teacher life **CAN'T** be beat
and if your teacher isn't sweet…

It's probably because they ran out of sprinkles
by the ice cream machine.

Poem in my Pocket

I got a poem in my pocket
a pocket full of poems,
words in my brain
and these words need homes,

so I scribble, I scrabble,
string them all together,
Keep in my pocket
just in case of bad weather,

or when I'm waiting in line
and I need to pass time
I just whip out a rhyme and read…
the poem in my pocket.

There's two in the front,
one in the back,
I even wrote a poem
on a wrapper from my snack.

Poems,
all these poems,
They keep falling out my head,
They're the stuffing in my pillow
when it's time to go to bed.

But the best place for them
where I know I'll never drop it,
is right by my side…safe in my pocket.

Nurses

(for Mrs. DeAndrea)

nurses work in ways
many don't understand

using intuition and healing powers
to cure illnesses,
better to be careful
than careless

an ice pack and band aid
work miracles
providing the perfect amount
of TLC to make it through another day

who else can handle microscopic paper cuts
and fallen out unbrushed baby teeth

taking temperatures, making calls,
and memorizing allergy lists
only scrape the surface of what they do

yes, they're overcautious,
germ conscious,
and want you to avoid avoidable accidents
BUT
Nurses care
in ways other people don't

School Music

(in the spirit of Arnold Adoff)

This School:

the constant **RING, RING, RINGING,**

feet stomping,

open

close.

SL a M

SH u T.

Back   Back

Forth   and   Forth

STAMPEDE

March,

March,

Marching,

uP & d
    o
      w
        n the halls,

bouncing off the walls.

ROARING like beasts!

HOWLING like wolves!

LUNCHTIME   IS   HERE!

whatif

(Mr. B's version after Shel Silverstein & Rasheed Adero)

Whatif Up was Down?
Whatif Black was White?
Whatif we put these guns down
and held each other tight?

Whatif war was just a card game
and hugs were like drugs?
Whatif the oceans were filled with laughter
and the continents with love?

Whatif racism never existed?
Man, wouldn't that be great?
Whatif we could flip our pencils over
and erase all this hate?

*What…if , What…if
What, What…if, if
What…if*

Whatif smartphones were dumb
and we had no choice but to think?
NO texting. NO Snapchat.
We'd all be forced to speak.

Whatif leaders stood united
and checked their egos at the door?
Whatif the rich weren't so rich
and felt the pain of being poor?

Whatif we stopped blaming others?
Whatif we cherished education?
Whatif respect was passed down
from generation to generation?

What…if, What…if
What, What…if, if
What…if

Whatif poets picked their poems off a poet tree?
Whatif YOU looked like HER.
and SHE looked like me?

Whatif vegetables tasted like candy?
Would broccoli rot your teeth?
Whatif schools weren't so test obsessed
and teachers could really teach?

Whatif I'm wrong?
Whatif I'm right?
Whatif we're running out of time?
Whatif we took the chip off our shoulders
and enjoyed the sunshine?

Whatif everything we see
isn't REALLY what it seems?
Whatif NOTHING is really real
and we're ALL living in a dream?

To my Baby Girl and Her Magical World,

If I could carry sunshine in my pocket,
>It would be you.

If I could,
>I would take your energy,

put it in a chocolate bar and make

E V E R Y O N E

>take a bite.

I would bottle your laughter

>and share it with *A L L* the sad people

>>in the world.

Maybe it would make them
>smile,

>>and play,

>>>and imagine,

>>>>and create,

>>>>>and live life carefree.

They could see the world
>as it is meant to be,

>>A CANVAS.

To glitter and glue,

      cut and color,

           NEVER JUDGE,

and LOVE and LOVE and LOVE and LOVE ...

Maybe they can create a U N I V E R S E

      that wears Unicorn capes,

Galaxy Boots,

      and WWE t-shirts.

LAUGHTER (BY JAMIE)

FREE!

      They could make slime,

squeeze squishies,

      have Barbie Doll Dream House sleepovers

          (No Kens Allowed!)

      and collect L.O.L Surprises that   cry,

                    spit,

           tinkle,

        or change colors

like the one you created… with Daddy's Money.

Love,

Your Forever ATM Machine.

The Teacher Blues

(a blues song for the Teachers)

da-na-na-na-na-nuh
My class is always talking,
da-na-na-na-na-nuh
My line is never straight,
da-na-na-na-na-nuh
It curves and loops
like a long winding snake.

That's the blues!
The afraid to walk my class
down the hallway blues!

da-na-na-na-na-nuh
Constantly calling out,
da-na-na-na-na-nuh
Always getting up,
da-na-na-na-na-nuh
They spread glue on my chair
now my B-U-T-T is stuck!

That's the blues!
My butt is stuck to my chair
and I have the blues

da-na-na-na-na-nuh

The copy machine jammed,

da-na-na-na-na-nuh

Couldn't run off my test,

da-na-na-na-na-nuh

When I told the class
they all screamed out, "YES!"

And that's the blues!
The I was so ready to make their lives miserable
with this MATH test blues!

da-na-na-na-na-nuh

Can't wait until 3 o'clock,

da-na-na-na-na-nuh

Then I'll be free!

da-na-na-na-na-nuh

But that's not happening,
because it's only 8:53!

That's the blues.
The please free Mr. B
from this classroom blues.

AND I don't know what to do
I feel like going BOO-HOO
It's only Monday morning
AND I got the blues,
The Teacher Blues!

Life-ku #3

Student: "It's not fair! It's not fair!"

Mr. B:

"If you want LIFE to
be FAIR, then take your behind
to a CARNIVAL!"

Judge Me Not

"Judge not by how you look, but by how you love."
-Sasha Smith, 3ʳᵈ grade, 2015

This is my belly.

It is not a pillow.
It is not a drum for you to beat,
or a magic lamp for you to rub.

It will **NOT** grant you wishes.
It is **JUST** a belly.

Caution.

Bumping into it
may send you flying across the room.

And before you ask…
NO, I am not pregnant,
Nor am I Santa's stunt double.

In my personal narrative,
fat is **NOT** a bad word, **CAN'T** is.
And I *CAN* lose weight.

BUT…it's tough to resist a good piece of cake.

This is who I am.
A third-grade teacher that looks
like he swallowed a beach ball,

in a school where students
pat me, poke me, bump me,
and rub my belly for good luck.

Lincoln had his beard,
George Washington had his teeth,
and I...
        have my belly.

So here's to the gentle giant that can't sit still,
to the little boy with extra thick lenses
that open his eyes to a wondrous world,

to the tiny angel,
strong, fearless, filled with courage
even with a beautiful, broken wing

you soar.

Here's to the girl. The hearing aid. The mic.
Magnifying sounds bringing them to life.

Take a minute.

Step away from the mirror.

Embrace your imperfections.

Wear them like armor
so no one can ever use them to hurt you.

The most important thing about love is...
it is always there,

but *YOU* must find it!

Be happy being you.

Be skinny, be nerdy,
be fat, be corny, be silly.

Nobody is perfect.
Nobody can *EVER* judge you.

Life is about the things you do.
That's what makes you, *YOU!*

Another This is Just to Say

This is Just to Say
I have eaten
EVERYTHING
in the icebox…

the plums,
      the apples,
the bananas,
      a dozen eggs,
2 packs of BACON,

          leftovers from yesterday's dinner,

          last week's meatballs,
the peanut butter,
      the jelly,
all the bread, aaaaaannnnd

the Snack Pack Chocolate Puddings
which you were probably saving
for the kids' school lunches.

FORGIVE ME!
But running around the world
at super speed
makes a **HERO** hungry!

By the way…
I also ate that greenish yellow fuzzy thing
I thought was a taco, **BUT NOW**, I'm not so sure.

Inside Mr. B's Stomach

I like donuts and cookies,

All that stuff is yummy to me.

But I HATE to eat my fruit and vegetables.

That is NASTY.

Poem and Illustration by a former unknown student

So You wanna BE A POET?

(inspired by Mikumari Caiyhe)

Some say poetry needs to RHYME,
Some say you need to write about NATURE,
Some even say poetry is the Language of Love,
BUT if you wanna be a poet...

First,
wrap yourself in a fancy scarf,
put on a beret,
take your shoes off,
grab a quill pen,

and begin TWISTING and TURNING
and TWIRLING your words
until your brain SCRAMBLES,
leaving you saying to yourself,

> "MY WORDS are AMAZING...
> LIKE A MAZE...
> *Like I am sooo LOST RIGHT NOW...*
> *I can't find my way out."*

Next,
use **coooool** words and L O N G words ALL THE TIME

and NEVER under,
ANY circumstance EVER
tell people what they mean!

Words like…

ULTRACREPIDARIAN,

CATTYWAMPUS, and

HIPPO-POTO-MONSTROSES-QUIPPE-DALIO-PHOBIA.

And at least once a week use your 'POETIC LICENSE'
to INVENT brand new words, like…

if you do something ridiculously awesome,
kind of like this poem, at the end yell,

'F A   B O O S H   K A '

After that,
speak in phrases like those REEEALLY old dead dudes did.

For example,
"Doth thee like eggs of green and ham?"
    "I doth not liketh yond Sam- of - I- am."
"Wouldst thee liketh those yolks hither or thither?"
    "I shalt not liketh thy eggs of green anywither."

Most importantly,
if you wanna **BE A POET**…
you must be DEEP and say DEEP things LIKE …

If a # 2 lead pencil is the most popular pencil in the world…
How come it's not # 1?

DEEP LIKE...

Why does Mickey Mouse treat Goofy like a human,
but Pluto like a dog?

Aren't they **BOTH** dogs !?

You must be bottom of the ocean DEEP LIKE ...

If parents say, *"Never take candy from strangers."*
Then, why do we bother celebrating Halloween?

BUT the truth is,

To be a poet…
You don't have to wrap yourself in a fancy scarf,
or write l o n g confusing made up words
 talking like really really old dead dudes,
 and you definitely don't have to be deep.

The truth is...
If you wanna be a Poet…
All you HAVE TO DO is pick up a pen
and write from the HEART...

FA BOOSH KA!

Life-ku #4

Student :   "I have to be partners with THEM!?"

Mr. B :

"LIFE and HAPPY MEALS...

Sometimes you get stuck with a

TOY... YOU... JUST... DON'T... WANT."

To the Lady that Does My Lesson Plans,

I just want **YOU** to know….
 "I LOVE YOU !"

You are the Tooth Fairy, Santa & Easter Bunny
rolled into a hardworking ball of A W E S O M E !

As I play and distract
　　　the already-distracted hive of Bees
you stay focused and work,
　　　　　　　　work,
　　　　　　　　　　WORK!
When Thursday comes you
　　　S L I D E perfect plans
under the principal's door and...

POOF!

　　　We are ready for the Magic of Monday!

　　　Through rain,
through sleet,
　　　through snow
YOU ALWAYS DELIVER!

Your lesson plans *ARE* my Glass Slipper
and I pray the clock NEVER

Tock-Ticks to midnight.

Cinderella has her *Fairy Godmother,*
        Peter Pan has *Tinker Bell,*
            Timmy Turner has *Fairly Odd Parents,*

and I have **YOU**...

my Lesson Plan fairy

From the Guy in the Hive

that would NEVER survive

without **YOU**.

by: Samantha Riccardo
2018

L.P. Fairy

12×1
4×5
7×3
8×5
3×7

They say

 NEVER strikes
the same place twice,

But your

Make the  shine,

the glow,

and my beat.

Thank u 4 being u

ROOM 20

A chuckle,

    a laugh,

a smile,

    a hug,

a lizard,

    some fish,

crunchy bugs,

    a me,

a you,

    a bee,

a buzz...

Welcome to Room 20

SPREAD some LOVE

Things I've Learned in 3rd Grade

College taught me absolutely NOTHING about teaching and even less about 8-year-olds. These are Things I've Learned in 3rd Grade.

1. I've learned which students put their hand up to answer questions and which ones need to use the bathroom.

    "What is 8 x 8? Kyle?"
    "Can I go to the bathroom?"

    You got me on that one.

2. There is a 285-pound weight limit to little chairs. Staring at the ceiling will make you rethink your diet, as the one caring student that isn't doubled over in a hyena-like convulsion comes over, pats you on the belly and says,

    "I think it's time to lose some weight big guy."

3. NEVER spell words with "pp" in it aloud. Stay away from the conjunction "but". When telling the class you have "Morning Duty", expect them to hold their noses and run away grossed out.

4. NEVER admit your mistakes. Respond with,

    "Ha! I was testing you!"

5. I've learned that I can bend time. With the right lessons I can make hours seem like minutes or minutes seem like years by simply saying,

   "You just lost 5 minutes of recess."

6. The simplest thoughts are the most profound…
   "Mr. B, segregation sounds very stupid."
   Indeed, Santiago, indeed.

7. Homework passes are like lottery tickets and smelly stickers are THE BEST form of bribery! They will make your line straighter, your classroom quieter, BUT they do not work with the sales person behind the counter or trying to get out of a speeding ticket.

8. I've learned that when you rip your pants in front of your class. They will offer you Post-its and masking tape to cover the hole. After this happens, they will ask to go to the bathroom so they can run class to class and tell EVERY SINGLE teacher, *"Mr. B ripped his pants and has masking tape on his butt!"*
   (Thank you, Katalina)

Some people learn from books, some learn from school.
   Me? I learn from 8-year-olds; it's a beautiful thing.

Acknowledgements

I am so grateful to the many people who have inspired, encouraged, supported and taught me throughout the years. I am very fortunate to have had two great mentors, Mike Chef-chik and Mary Ellen Martko. They saw the passion I had for teaching and molded me into the teacher I am today. They, along with Patty Valese, introduced me to the importance of poetry in the classroom and beyond. Every lesson I teach and poem I recite is because of their belief in me.

I must acknowledge and thank every student I have ever taught for believing in me as a teacher. You keep me going! Thank you, Sarah and Sasha, for inspiring *What Teachers REALLY Do* and *Judge Me Not.* Lauren, Samantha, and Logan thank you for your artwork. There is no better place to be than school!

To the entire Roosevelt Elementary School family, Mr. Diehl, the District of South Plainfield and every teacher who accepts me for who I am, thank you. To the Community of South Plainfield, Nancy, Jean and Sue at the South Plainfield Observer, Charlie and Deb for supporting young writers, and every Junior Journalist Winner, thank you for allowing me to share my voice over the years.

For many of my years in the classroom, Vera Agee and Lauren Wentworth taught by my side. They embraced my non-traditional approach to education and for that I thank you both!

I cannot express how appreciative I am for the help and support of Sue Hyun (the brains to my beauty) and Melanie Glowacki … this book is yours as much as it is mine. From day one, you ladies were ALL IN with me. Also, I would not have been able to complete this project without the assistance of Viviana Salgado and Tehsuan Glover from Studio Creative Group. Special thank you to Omar Holman and Lizz Straight for patiently guiding me through the editing process and Joseph Thomas, Kirk Nugent, James C. Ellerbe and Kyla Jenee Lacey for offering valuable feedback.

Bringing my students' writing beyond the page has always been important to me as an educator but would NEVER happen without my super techie teachers... Mrs. Stoeckel, Mrs. Brandenburg and Mrs. Noland. Thank you for pushing me and helping create memorable, life-long learning moments for so many students.

To the many poets who have inspired me and to those who have become true family, my appreciation for you runs deep. I never thought performing poetry would provide me with so many opportunities and friendships.

Everyone needs a strong support system. I want to thank my mother and father for always supporting everything I have ever done. My sister, Grace, for never judging me *(at least I think she never judges me)*, Rob, Haley, Ally, Jessica and the kids, and my nieces and nephews. To my friends, my family: Big Jeff, Demetrius, Nick, Cory, Flow, Gem, Myra, Margaret, Samantha, Allison, Rob Hylton, DJ Irs, Omar and Ian, Starski and Viv, Mahogany Brown and Jive Poetic, the New Jeru Slam Team, Nourish and Helena D. Lewis... I love you all! You guys mean the world to me.

And to my family...

Madelyn, I am amazed at your strength and positive attitude when faced with adversity. You have given me the freedom to find my voice. I hope our children can mirror your confidence and unbreakable spirit. Brandon and Devon, I am honored you both call me, "Dad." I could not ask for better sons... and to my godson, Darius, you are a KING, a MIRACLE, and a BEAUTIFUL SOUL, living life in the moment as it is meant to be.

Finally, to my baby girl, Jamie...

You are everything this world is missing.

This is for you.

About the Illustrators

Jamie Bertram is an eleven-year-old artist from Rahway, NJ. She loves drawing, arts and crafts, and spending her dad's money. She enjoys making fan edits on Instagram and wears WWE t-shirts every day. When asked what she wants to do in the future, she states, "I don't know! I'm only 11!"

Melanie Glowacki graduated from Kean University and currently teaches Pre-K through 4th grade Art in South Plainfield, NJ. She has a passion for photography and interior design, but her ability to inspire and awaken the creativity in students is a gift that will shape the future artists of the world.

Connect with Mr. B:
Email : bigmikemrb@gmail.com
Twitter : @poet_teacher
Instagram: @mr.bpoetry
Facebook: Said the Paper to the Pen

Photograph taken by Ameerah Shabazz-Bilal

Write your own poem here:

35192146R00047

Made in the USA
San Bernardino, CA
07 May 2019